D1616554

www.vigodabooks.com
Copyright TXu 2-153-797 (2019)

First Edition

ISBN - 978-1-7370629-0-5

Seasons Change and So Do I

Written by
Carol Vigoda-Fuchs

Illustrated by
Lori Rosen

Johnny is sitting at his desk, staring at the
picture of Grandma, Uncle Jaime and himself.
He puts his hands to his head and wants to cry.

He thinks to himself,
"Uncle Jaime doesn't come and
play with me anymore, I miss him."

Johnny is peering out of the window.

He says to God,
"You are my blue sky,
you are my sunny day.
Thank you."

Mommy calls to Johnny to get ready
to go in the pool.

Excited, Johnny can't wait to get outside.
He puts on his bathing suit.

Out on the lawn in the backyard, Johnny asks Mommy a concerning question, "Where is Uncle Jaime? Why doesn't he come to my house and visit anymore?"

"Look up Johnny, look!"
As Mommy points to the sky,

"Uncle Jaime is climbing the 'Stairway to Heaven'. His spirit will hear you and guide you."

Preparing to jump off the diving board, Johnny is overcome with a warm peaceful feeling.

Not only does he get goose bumps, but he spots
a majestic, iridescent dragonfly. All excited, he shouts
and points; "Look Mommy, a dragonfly."

Mommy begins to explain to Johnny,
"It takes five years for a dragonfly to
be. It is a long and painful journey."

Lunchtime Mommy is serving Johnny a peanut butter and jelly sandwich on the picnic table on the deck.

About to take his first bite, he sees a dragonfly fluttering its purple and blue wings are illuminated by the sunlight.

An excited Johnny, screams, "It's Uncle Jaime. He came to have lunch with me."

Later that day, Johnny is looking up at his bedroom window. And what does he see?

Why, right there, outside his window is the same iridescent dragonfly fluttering its wings. Johnny is sure it is the same one he saw twice today.

Johnny heads to his bedroom. His windows had been left open.
He enters his bedroom and to Johnny's great excitement
right there on his table, is the dragonfly.

It is sitting on the
picture of Uncle Jaime.
Johnny squeals with delight,
"Uncle Jaime, you came to
play with me!"

Outside on the deck Johnny sits on the steps while watching Daddy and Grandma. They are so busy assembling the bird feeder and filling it with food, they don't notice Johnny.

The leaves have changed colors and fallen from the trees. Winter is coming and food will be scarce for the birds.

Johnny decides to go to his bedroom to play.
The Legos are still out on the floor with his matchbox cars.
He places the picture of Jaime against the Lego container and
sits down to play. Johnny talks to the picture, "Uncle Jaime, why
don't you sit with me like you did in the summer? I miss you!"

Darkness approaches and it's bedtime.

Johnny kneels beside his bed and says his prayers
with Grandma tonight. Johnny recites his blessings
to God and ends with, "God, I am going to cry all
night because I miss Uncle Jaime."

Morning arrives and the sun brings light into the room. Grandma wakes Johnny up from his sleep, only to find Johnny with red, swollen eyes. Grandma understands! She takes Johnny's hand, "Come, honey, I want to show you something."

Hand in hand they arrive at the sliding
glass doors to the deck.

Grandma and Johnny press their
noses against the glass.

Johnny sees two cardinals, a male
and a female, eating at the
bird feeders.

Grandma explains how cardinals are
a sign that someone you miss
is saying, "I love you."

The next day and the days following, the two red
cardinals come to eat, rest on the deck and the nearby
branches. Grandma says, "Those we love don't go
away, they walk beside us every day."

Each day, Johnny and Grandma hear the
cardinals singing their song.

Grandma says, "Their song almost sounds as
though they are saying 'cheer'."

While the family is asleep, the first snowfall arrives. Johnny peers out his snowy window and watches the snow as it falls.

Excited, he quickly dresses into his blue snowsuit and boots. For a fleeting moment, he wonders about the birds.

Everyone is sleeping and it is quiet. In the
backyard, the snow is fresh and untouched.
Johnny is building a snowman.

Just as Johnny steps away to admire his work, he spots the red cardinal landing on the snowman's carrot nose.

The cardinal's mate watches from a snowy branch. Johnny squeals with excitement, "Uncle Jaime, you came to play with me."

Johnny is five years old.
His daddy taught him how
important it is to be dressed
in full, protective
riding gear.

He is wearing his yellow
safety suit with the cool
design, black boots, red gloves
and most importantly,
his black helmet.

The sun is shining. It is a cool, invigorating day.
The garage door is open. Johnny's orange KTM dirt bike
with the black seat sits waiting for Johnny to celebrate
the first day of spring.

Johnny is excited because he is going to ride today.
"I wish Uncle Jaime was here to watch me ride,"
thinks Johnny.

Johnny is doing some whoop-de-dos on the dirt and hills in the backyard taking many practice laps around his yard.

He is preparing himself to do some stunts. Daddy will be taking Johnny to the racetrack soon.

Johnny hits a bump, loses control of his dirt bike and starts sliding. He goes over the handlebars and hits the dirt. He sure was acting "squirrely".

Long legged daddy hears the crash and comes running.

With a tear in his eye, a puckered lip and a softness in his voice, Johnny cries out, "I ate the dirt, Daddy."

Lifting his face from the dirt, Johnny sees a black beetle.
Johnny says to his daddy, "Look, Daddy!
There is a beetle, it has hearts on it."

A smile appears
on Johnny's face.
Johnny says, "Daddy, it's
Uncle Jaime telling me
I am okay."

The sun shines on the beetle as it lies in the dirt. To Daddy's astonishment, he sees the four yellow hearts on the beetle glistening in the light.

Daddy takes his phone out of his pocket and snaps a picture of the beetle.

That evening at the dinner table, Johnny tells the
story how he "ate the dirt today." Daddy takes out his
cell phone. He shows Mommy the picture of the beetle.

Mommy's eyes light up and in her wise voice explains,
"Beetles protect you and keep you safe; just like Uncle
Jaime keeps you safe."

LIFE CYCLE OF THE DRAGONFLY

The nymph comes out of the egg and spends five years under the surface of the water. Using its' gills to breathe and jaws to get its food. When the nymph is ready to metamorphosis into an adult, it climbs up a piece of vegetation in the evening. As morning arrives, the dragonfly molts by crawling out of its old larval skin. Now It is free to fly into a bright new world. The dragonfly's long and painful journey is over. The dragonfly is the keeper of our dreams, potential and emotions. Be Free!

LIFE CYCLE OF THE CARDINAL IS A JOURNEY.

The Male and Female must find each other and mate for life. The female lays the eggs and they both must protect the eggs from predators. Once, they hatch, the journey is not over until the baby bird can fly away and leave the nest. The cycle begins again. Cardinals are spiritual messengers who have been sent by our loved ones in Heaven to watch over us. They have a deep connection to lost souls. After the death of a loved one, cardinals are sent with a message letting us know that those we love don't go away, they walk beside us every day.

LIFE CYCLE OF THE SCARAB BEETLE

There is great planning; underground structures must be made with a supply of rolled dung to house and feed the young, as they metamorphosis into an adult. Beetles assure you that you are on the right path in life. When a beetle appears, it is here to tell you that you are not ordinary, there is magic, creativity and imagination in you waiting to be released. You can achieve great things; but you must discover your own way. You choose. Do not follow, lead. The Beetle is here to protect and keep you safe.

THE
NEVERENDING

ABOUT THE AUTHOR CAROL VIGODA-FUCHS:

Carol Vigoda-Fuchs is an independent, life-affirming and humorous lady from New Jersey. She is the daughter of the American actor Abe Vigoda, that tall, charismatic, dour-faced figure with slouched shoulders who is well-known through film and television. Inspired by her father's work and endowed with a generous portion of humour, she wrote her first play at the age of ten years. At that time, it was successfully performed at the Robert Fulton School in North Bergen, New Jersey.

Since then she has never lost her passion for writing. As a mother to three sons, aunt to two nieces and a grandmother to two boys, her home is always open to children for whom she thinks up numerous stories. "Seasons Change and So Do I" is her first published book. It was written in honor of her deceased son and plays a great role in her mourning process.

Carol Vigoda-Fuchs spends a lot of her time outdoors in the country to which she has a close relationship. She finds consolation in the small signs she perceives, such that can mend the tears in her soul and afford her some peace.

Carol's grandson Johnathan also perceives these signs. The story is told through his eyes and with the five-year-old's words as well as some of his own photographs.

CPSIA information can be obtained
at www.ICGtesting.com
Printed in the USA
BVHW090754190422
634307BV00002B/9